WHAT IS A
Friend?

WHAT IS A
Friend?

by
Sylvia Vardell
+
Janet Wong

Pomelo
Books

100% of the profits from this book
will be donated
to the IBBY Children in Crisis Fund

The IBBY Children in Crisis Fund provides support for children
whose lives have been disrupted through war, civil disorder, or
natural disaster. The program gives immediate support and help –
and also aims for long-term community impact, aligning with IBBY's
goal of giving every child the right to become a reader.

ibby.org/awards-activities/ibby-children-in-crisis-fund
usbby.org/donate.html

Special thanks to Renée M. LaTulippe for her ongoing help in editing
Pomelo Books publications.

This book is dedicated to Liz Page, former Executive Director of
IBBY and a good friend to children around the world.

Pomelo Books
9440 Viewside Drive
Dallas, TX 75231
PomeloBooks.com
info@pomelobooks.com

Library of Congress Cataloging-in-Publication Data is available.
ISBN 978-1-937057-16-9

Please visit us:
PomeloBooks.com

POEMS BY

Gail Aldous

Marcie Flinchum Atkins

Robyn Hood Black

Willeena Booker

Sandy Brehl

Carol Bullman

Kelly Conroy

Mary E. Cronin

Linda A. Dryfhout

Janet Clare Fagal

Karen Elise Finch

Nancy Bo Flood

Patricia J. Franz

Marilyn Garcia

Van G. Garrett

Theresa Gaughan

Sara Holbrook

Irene Latham

Rebecca Gardyn Levington

Molly Lorenz

Jone Rush MacCulloch

Carmela A. Martino

Guadalupe García McCall

Rochelle Melander

Heidi Mordhorst

Elisabeth Norton

Joan Riordan

Laura Purdie Salas

René Saldaña, Jr.

Michael Salinger

Donna JT Smith

Anastasia Suen

Pamela Taylor

Linda Kulp Trout

Fernanda Valentino

Charles Waters

Vicki Wilke

Matthew Winter

Janet Wong

Helen Kemp Zax

Sarah Ziman

TABLE OF CONTENTS

TABLE OF CONTENTS

FRIEND
by Janet Wong

Uncle Johnny is my best friend
on weeknights.
We sit with our feet up on the couch
and play games
while we watch TV.

Uncle Jimmy is my best friend
on weekends.
He shows me things
like how to make volcanoes
out of candle wax.

Jenny is my best friend
at school, but she thinks
I'm not making sense.
She believes family can't be friends.
I say, *Tell me then: What is a friend?*

RESCUE

by Linda Kulp Trout

At first,
he was scared,
so was I.

He just stood there
staring
with eyes that said
life hasn't been easy –
his scars deep as mine.

I reached for him.
He moved closer,
his breath
warm on my face.

I don't know his name,
so I just call him
Friend.

TRUST

by Gail Aldous

She has a soft voice.
She does not yell at me.
Her touch is gentle and warm.

My friend gives me food in my *own* bowl.
I don't need to share. I am not hungry
all the time, anymore.

I can sleep in her bed.
I like listening to her breathe
as she falls asleep holding me.

She holds me close in her hands,
kisses me, my nose to her nose.
Her smile brightens my day and my night.

I trust her.

14

HERE

by Rebecca Gardyn Levington

Across the miles,
I smile, you smile.
We share. We laugh.
We chat a while.

It's not the same,
I understand.
I'd rather hug you,
hold your hand.

But thanks to cool
technology,
you're always "here"
right next to me.

TOGETHER

by Irene Latham

My best friend lives in another town,
so we connect by screen.

We laugh together, finish homework,
share stories & dreams.

When time comes to say goodbye,
my best friend who felt so near

       suddenly
       disappears.

A tidal wave of loneliness
slams into my day.

That's when my cat finds my lap.
She rubs & bumps my hand.

A good friend knows just what to say –
Purrrrrrr. Here I am.

LUNCH
by Molly Lorenz

Lunch in hand:
Where should I sit?
I look around:
Where do I fit?

Kids huddle at the end of rows.
Kids laugh and chat nearby.
One new girl sits all alone
with no friends by her side.

I think I'll sit with her today.
I'll smile and say hello.
And as we munch and crunch our lunch
a friendship just might grow.

NEW
by Karen Elise Finch

Free to be loud,
raised hands holler,
    Hey! Over here!

I follow the laughter
of friends
who welcome me
to join in,
laugh in,
grow in
my new
home.

JUMP

by Matthew Winter

Turn, turn, turn.
Turn the rope around.
Hear. It. Hit. And.
Slap. The. Ground.

Once you learn the beat,
the rhythm of the spin –
on your mark, get set, and –
Jump. Right. In.

Slappity, clappity,
spin and hop,
around and around,
I just can't stop –

I boing and bounce
just like a spring.
Watch. Me. Now.
I'm the jump rope king!

SELFIE

by Willeena Booker

Meet my magnificent crew!
my number 1 and my number 2
always there when cheering up
is what I need to do

Pose. Smile. Click. REPEAT!
Pose. Smile. Click. REPEAT!

When tough days steal my thunder
when I feel like I'm going under
I just need to call my crew
my number 1 and my number 2

One look at my friends
and the laughter begins
Pose. Smile. Click. REPEAT!
my besties will come through for me

SIT-UPS

by Rochelle Melander

Last time we did sit-ups,
I flopped. Kids laughed.
Why would I do that again?
But Milo's eyes encourage me:
"You can do it, friend."
And with his help
I can.

PRESENT
by Robyn Hood Black

You didn't say,
   Come on – Cheer up!
   Things are going to be okay.

You didn't say,
   I know exactly
   what it's like
   to feel that way.

You didn't say
   anything.

Just sat with me,

  and
    that
      meant
        everything.

GAMERS
by Pamela Taylor

Gamers are
Aiming to
Master
Each level

Onward and upward
Victorious – and
Earning each other's
Respect

SIDEKICKS
by Carmela A. Martino

Side by side,
we have learned:
      front kicks,
      back kicks,
      roundhouse kicks,

      hook kicks,
      push kicks,
      crescent kicks,

      axe kicks,
      knee kicks,
      spinning kicks.

Along the way,
we have become
the very best . . .
           sidekicks.

CHECKMATE

by Fernanda Valentino

We sit and stare at each other.
Pieces wait in perfect rows,
bracing for combat.

We're in a battle of wits and smarts –
with carefully planned and aggressive moves –
protecting the king against
the opponent's surprise attacks.

We are strategic warriors.
Ruthless block!
Clever retreat and castle!

Our dueling cuts through the silence.
Checkmate. Game over.

Rivalry aside,
we retrace our brilliant moves
along with our silly blunders.

And go back to simply being
best friends.
Ready, set,

REMATCH!

SWISH

by Nancy Bo Flood

He's older,
bigger.
Doesn't matter.

I'm smaller, younger but quick when I
pivot,
spin,
dribble past.
Fake the next move.
Look right,
go left.
Set up a jump shot,
aim,
shoot . . .

The ball spins round and round the rim
until . . .

SWISH!

WINNING

by Elisabeth Norton

Walking onto the court changes us
from friends
to rivals
serving, volleying, defending the net,
trying to score points
against each other,

game after game after game,
set after set after set,
until finally
it's match point,
your serve –
and you ace it.

You won the match,
but with a friend like you
I'm a winner too.

SUPPORT

by Sarah Ziman

You know they'll always have your back –
they lift you up, keep you on track.
They're on your side,
through thick and thin –
the days you lose and those you win.

Sometimes you'll follow, sometimes lead,
but keep them close, and you'll succeed.
No girl's an island,
that is true –
and like a ship, she needs her crew.

So do your best and play your part –
extending hands is just the start.
Support each other,
share that dream –
and that's how friends become a team.

TEAM

by Mary E. Cronin

We plan,
we code,
we try, fail,
adjust.

We program,
tinker,
argue, solve,
trust.

We do
a trial run,
we double-check,
correct.

Building on
each other's strengths,
we got this –
we connect.

ACTION

by Linda A. Dryfhout

The school play opens tonight.
Props are out, lights are bright.
Costumes, sound effects are set.
It's so hot we start to sweat.

Standby! Places! Music starts!
We know all our lines by heart.
Curtain rises – start the show.
Our best friends? In the first row!

LAUGHTER

by Helen Kemp Zax

We are laughing so hard
I might split in two.
Then there'd be more of me –
One for you.
                One for you.

INSTEAD

by Sara Holbrook

Studies.
Tension.
Social.
Stress.
Taking so much in!

Puddles.
Splashing.
Flapping.
Laughing.
Letting it all out!

FREEWHEELING

by Michael Salinger

Two wheels times two make four.
We soar
through our neighborhood,
its alleys and trails,
hands gripping our bars,
feet pumping our pedals,
the wind in our faces.
Cycling never fails
to make us feel free –
alone,
together,
just you
and me.

STORYTELLING

by Van G. Garrett

Our thoughts float
Like bubbles
When we circle
Laughing the hours away

Making mountains
Of memories
To warm us
When times turn *wintry*

JITTERS

by Laura Purdie Salas

How will I stand?
What if I fall?
What if I trip and crash
into the wall?

My legs go all twisty.
My gut's like a stone.
But at least I'm not here at the rink
all alone.

I pull on my gloves.
I grip my friend's hand.
He's rock-solid steady,
and I (sort of . . . mostly) stand.

Then I'm spinning –
I'm sliding –
and finally, I fall.
But we're laughing
so hard –

I don't care at all!

OLLIE

by Jone Rush MacCulloch

Skateboard park
The day is hot

Frontside ollie
Ready or not

Surfing the streets
Shredding the ramp

Next level
Mastered all that

Ollie
With a twist

Crouch
Jump the board

Pivot
The body

While friends
Record

STOKED

by Joan Riordan

Hey Goofy-foot,

Glad you joined
the thrashers at
the bowl

practicing your
ollies and
alley-oops.

It looked like
arm-slinging,
smile-wringing,
friend-making
fun.

Happy to be
your mate
when you sk8.

Your rad-and-ready
Brain Bucket

ALIVE

by Marilyn Garcia

My stick and I
pause
pose
plot
plan

Whistle blows

My stick and I
come alive
on this grassy field

My stick and I
pivot, dodge, sprint, run
burn the field like the blazing sun

My stick and I
pass and check
cradle and scoop
catch
aim
SHOOT!

MYSELF
by Heidi Mordhorst

Surrounded by
people – motion – color – noise
I turn away from the blur and

       suddenly with a jolt

   I realize
   I am my favorite person,
   my own best friend.

When I'm alone,

      nothing is missing.

I can sit with myself,
with my thoughts
careening peacefully around

     the pavilion of my mind,

   bumping again and again
   into my favorite person,
   myself, my own best friend.

TREASURED

by Carol Bullman

Braiding strands of friendship,
Of tenderness, time, and trust –

In your gentle fingers
My hair is a treasure, rare.

Weave in your magic, bestie . . .
The beauty you see in me.

AMIGUITA

by Guadalupe García McCall

A friend is an amiguita you might meet
at school, on the bus, or in the pool.
You may run into them at the park when
you walk your Chucho around the block.

When an amiguita comes over, she may bring
her Mami, or her brother, or her poodle, Noodle.
She might bring cookies, cake, or even a pie.
She might also bring fears, worries, or a gentle sigh.

A friend might want to play with all your toys.
She may even touch things you dearly adore
and leave her smudgy fingerprints all over
the windows of your Mami's car door.

Sometimes, an amiguita takes your muñeco,
Momo, home by mistake because it got lost
inside the chaos stuffed in her overnight bag.
Don't worry, just call her. She'll bring it right back.

A friend is more than someone who is
always borrowing your bright barrettes.
An amiguita checks to make sure your lab
goggles are straight, protecting your face.

HAPPY

by René Saldaña, Jr.

Julieta got so sick she missed
her own birthday party. But
now, Julieta's gotten un-sick.

She's got some color back to her,
a smile on her face again.

Honoka, Johnny, and me
have a surprise for her:
a piñata in the shape of a star,

the shiny ribbons blowing
in the breeze like it's shooting across the sky.

Julieta can't eat candies, so
we've filled the star with mounds
and mounds of green confetti.

Green's her favorite color. So
when she smashes it, all of it

rains down on us, the sun happy
on our faces, Julieta brighter than any star.
The confetti blowing makes it look

like she's floating up. She reaches out her hands
to us, the four of us floating up together.

PROMISE
by Marcie Flinchum Atkins

We promise

  to ride the waves to the shore
  to celebrate a frothy tumble
  to float the day away
  to dig our toes into the sand
  to freeze while fish dart between our legs
  to swim until we wrinkle

CAMPING

Janet Clare Fagal

Look says the tent:
there's hiking,
swimming,
gathering.

Listen says the tent:
do you hear the silence,
sweet birdsong,
waves lapping?

Breathe says the tent:
the air is sweet
with the scent
of firs.

Learn says the tent:
nature
is
whispering.

WAIT!

by Sandy Brehl

We shimmy into shallows,
this weedy wilderness below the pier.
Those boys are back,
toting rods, hooks, and pails.

Don't bite! Just WAIT!
That's not a bug, it's BAIT!
They've mastered patience,
sensing we are near.

Stay in the shadows, still.
They're not willing to head home
with empty hands.
No more tales
of ones that got away.

We wait.
They wait.

Stalemate.

EXPLORERS

by Theresa Gaughan

We're the great explorers
Walking through the trees
Backpacks loaded full of gear
Dodging honeybees

Seeing nature's beauty
Laughing all the while
Glad we have our boots on
Hiking lots of miles

Summer day explorers
Bonding as we talk
Bodies, minds, and friendship
Strengthened by a walk

COPILOT

by Kelly Conroy

You wait for me each morning.
I wait for you each day.
We slowly cruise the side streets since
we have so much to say.

We navigate the present.
We chart our futures too.
I'm glad I travel back and forth
to school each day with you.

SIBLINGS

by Donna JT Smith

I climb the highest branches.
You build fairy homes below.
I like water-skiing jets.
You prefer to row.

We both like dogs and horses.
And reading mystery books.
You're the one who likes to sleep,
while I'm the one who cooks!

Sometimes we have an argument.
We yell and stomp and pout!
But pretty soon it's all resolved.
"What was that all about?"

Let no one come between us.
Let no one dare offend.
I'll defend my sister:
She's my forever friend!

REMEMBERING
by Vicki Wilke

We stand, side by side –
measuring, mixing, smiling,
remembering
Grandpa's cinnamon sweet bread.

Shoulder to shoulder,
we tiptoed on stools,
peered in as he poured the ingredients
into a large, blue-flowered bowl.

We helped crack eggs,
only dropped a few –
but Grandpa didn't mind.

The best part was kneading.
We waited excitedly
to hold the warm, stretchy dough.

He taught us to s-q-u-e-e-z-e with care –
to become a part of it,
like we were part of him.

Kneading the dough,
we remember.

BREAKFAST
by Charles Waters

I hope he liked breakfast.

          Breakfast hit the spot!

Omelets are his favorite.

          That was so rad of him.

His gift for making honor roll.

          He always has my back.

He's never far from my mind.

          I think about him a lot.

I wish I could say . . .

          I wish I could say . . .

          I love you.

SERVICE

by Anastasia Suen

Soccer sisters
Even off the field
Relaxing together after we
Volunteer
In our
Community – a team of friends
Each time we meet

IMAGINE

by Patricia J. Franz

With you I learn to listen.
With you I find my voice.
Together we can dream
a better world, a different choice.

Together we are Courage.
We don't stand or fight alone.
Champions together;
we can't do it on our own.

I don't know the answers,
just the possibilities.
Imagine, together,
what we might achieve!

RESOURCES
FOR
READERS
AND
WRITERS

WAYS TO SHARE POEMS WITH A FRIEND

Sometimes you want to write a poem just for yourself and keep it private. But other times it's fun to share your poem with a friend, with someone else who also likes to write, or with the whole wide world. Here are some ways to share your poem.

For "Poem in Your Pocket Day" write your own poem or a favorite poem on small cards to give away and to keep in your pocket to share whenever you like.

Copy or write your favorite poem or your own original poem on a postcard or letter and mail it to a friend. Or make a postcard with your poem and art on one side and the friend's address on the other – and then mail it!

Find a poetry pen-pal and pass your favorite poems or your own original poems back and forth. Make a book of the poems you share with each other.

If you can text on a phone, try arranging your text message as a poem with line breaks or sharing your own poem in a text message. Or take a picture of your poem and send it with a text message.

Videotape yourself reading your poem out loud and send it to a friend. Or do an audio recording of yourself reading your poem and share the audio file with a friend.

Why not turn a blank card into a greeting card for a special occasion by writing your own poem on it and then adding your message to send to a friend?

Arrange your poem into a special gift. Write it on special paper, add a drawing or painting or print a picture, and frame it as a present for someone special.

If you like using your computer to make art, collaborate with a friend to use digital tools to create a collage or poster of a poem you write together and take turns picking the images you both like best.

Make your poem into 3-D art. Write each line of your poem on a different piece of heavy paper, then put a string through each separate piece and hang them each on a stick or rod to make a poem mobile.

Work with a friend to turn a favorite poem (or an original poem) into a poem for two voices. Decide who will read which line and which lines you'll read together; then record your reading to share with others.

WEB RESOURCES

Here are some of our favorite poetry-related websites to explore, with information about poets, sample poems and activities, tips and games, and much more.

Giggle Poetry
GigglePoetry.com
*A fun site with poems plus activities, games, and poem scripts.

No Water River
by Renée M. LaTulippe
NoWaterRiver.com
*Watch videos of poets reading and talking about their poetry.

Pinterest/PomeloBooks
Pinterest.com/PomeloBooks.com
*Digital postcards featuring poems.

Poetry for Kids
by Kenn Nesbitt
Poetry4Kids.com
*A "poetry playground" with funny poems.

Poetry Foundation
PoetryFoundation.org
*Sponsor of the Young People's Poet Laureate program, with a searchable database that includes some poems for young people.

The Dirigible Balloon
DirigibleBalloon.org
*A webzine publishing poems that take "young readers on a journey, lifting their thoughts, feelings and aspirations as though they were on an exciting flight."

The Poetry Minute
PoetryMinute.org
*You'll find a poem for every day, Monday through Friday, from September through June.

POETRY BOOKS ABOUT FRIENDSHIP

Friends and friendship are such an important part of life. Many poetry books focus on this topic, including the following.

Cheng, Andrea. 2008. *Where the Steps Were.*
*Five students narrate the issues they're dealing with during the school year.

Florian, Douglas. 2018. *Friends and Foes: Poems About Us All.*
*Twenty-three witty poems about the ups and downs of friendship.

Frost, Helen. 2014. *Room 214: A Year in Poems.*
*Poems in twenty-two forms reveal the feelings of a class of fifth-grade students.

Greenfield, Eloise. 2006. *The Friendly Four.*
*Four friends spend a summer together in discovery and play.

Grimes, Nikki. 2016. *Garvey's Choice.*
*Garvey is overweight and struggles with his relationship with his dad; friendship and music help.

Herrick, Steven. 2008. *Naked Bunyip Dancing.*
*A creative teacher draws out the best in each of his students through drama, music, and play.

Holbrook, Sara. 2011. *Weird? (Me, Too!) Let's Be Friends.*
*An honest and heartwarming collection of poems about friendship.

Hunter, Jane McMorland. 2019. *Friends: A Poem for Every Day of the Year.*
*365 classic and contemporary poems about the nature of friendship and its joys and complications.

Latham, Irene and Waters, Charles. 2017. *Can I Touch Your Hair? Poems of Race, Mistakes, and Friendship.*
*Two kids – one white, one black – explore race and become friends.

Levy, Debbie. 2010. *The Year of Goodbyes: A True Story of Friendship, Family and Farewells.*
*Poems explore the everyday life of a Jewish girl in Germany in 1938.

Park, Linda Sue. 2021. *The One Thing You'd Save.*
*A classroom of diverse kids contemplate what's most important to each of them through these poems.

Prasadam-Halls, Smriti. 2020. *I'm Sticking with You.*
*A poem picture book about a bear and squirrel who discover being together is best, even when friends can be annoying.

Quattlebaum, Mary. 2005. *Winter Friends.*
*This story-in-poems captures friends having fun during winter weather.

Quattlebaum, Mary. 2019. *Brother, Sister, Me and You.*
*Human siblings and animal siblings are paired through movement and play.

Raczka, Bob. 2010. *Guyku: A Year of Haiku for Boys.*
*Haiku poems capture a year of boys having fun in nature.

Shovan, Laura. 2016. *The Last Fifth Grade of Emerson Elementary.*
*A class of fifth-graders bonds together as they find their voice and stand up for what they believe in.

Vardell, Sylvia and Wong, Janet. 2017. *Here We Go.*
*A group of four friends works together to improve their school and their community.

Wardlaw, Lee. 2015. *Won Ton and Chopstick: A Cat and Dog Tale Told in Haiku.*
*An opinionated cat becomes friends with the new pup in the family.

Wong, Janet S. 2003. *Minn and Jake.*
*Minn and Jake become best friends while catching lizards.

Wong, Janet. 2008. *Minn and Jake's Almost Terrible Summer.*
*Minn and Jake navigate the difficulties of friendship.

Love is the only force capable of transforming an enemy into a friend.
Dr. Martin Luther King, Jr.

EKPHRASTIC POETRY BOOKS

The books on this list feature poetry written in response to art, called "ekphrastic" poetry.

Brenner, Barbara. Ed. 2000. *Voices: Poetry and Art from Around the World.*
*Poems representing six continents focus on culture, history, or land through art.

Greenberg, Jan. 2001. *Heart to Heart: New Poems Inspired by Twentieth-Century American Art.*
*Paintings, sculpture, and photographs by 20th-century American artists inspire these poems.

Greenberg, Jan. 2008. *Side by Side: New Poems Inspired by Art from Around the World.*
*Poems in their original language and in English accompany global art from ancient Egypt to modern Sweden.

Hopkins, Lee Bennett. Ed. 2018. *World Make Way: New Poems Inspired by Art from the Metropolitan Museum of Art.*
*Poems by eighteen poets inspired by some of the most popular art in the collection of The Metropolitan Museum.

Lewis, J. Patrick and Yolen, Jane. 2011. *Self-Portrait with Seven Fingers: A Life of Marc Chagall in Verse.*
*Fourteen of Chagall's famous paintings are the inspiration for poems by these two poets.

Rochelle, Belinda. Ed. 2001. *Words with Wings: A Treasury of African-American Poetry and Art.*
*Twenty African American poets explore twenty works of art by African American artists on themes of slavery, racism, and pride.

Vardell, Sylvia and Wong, Janet. 2022. *Things We Eat.*
*Poets use photo prompts to explore a wide variety of foods from avocados to kimchi to quiche to zucchini.

Vardell, Sylvia and Wong, Janet. 2022. *Things We Feel.*
*Poets use photo prompts to explore emotions through poetry, describing feelings of being happy, frustrated, lonely, proud, scared, zany, and more.

POETS WRITE ABOUT WRITING

Several poets have written books ABOUT poetry writing for young people. Here are a few that might be helpful.

Fletcher, Ralph J. 2005. *A Writing Kind of Day: Poems for Young Poets*.
*How to write a poem about almost anything with tips on every step of the creative process.

Holbrook, Sara, Salinger, Michael, and Harvey, Stephanie. 2018. *From Striving to Thriving Writers: Strategies that Jump-Start Writing*.
*Twenty-seven writing strategies and lessons targeting reading, writing, and speaking.

Janeczko, Paul B., comp. 2002. *Seeing the Blue Between: Advice and Inspiration for Young Poets*.
*A poetry collection with poems and advice from 32 poets.

Lawson, JonArno. 2008. *Inside Out: Children's Poets Discuss Their Work*.
*Twenty-three poets sharing poems and explaining how the poem came to be.

Prelutsky, Jack. 2008. *Pizza, Pigs, and Poetry: How to Write a Poem*.
*The poet sharing how he creates poems from anecdotes, often using comic exaggeration.

Salas, Laura Purdie. 2011. *Picture Yourself Writing Poetry: Using Photos to Inspire Writing*.
*A clear and engaging approach with writing prompts and mentor texts.

Wolf, Allan. 2006. *Immersed in Verse: An Informative, Slightly Irreverent & Totally Tremendous Guide to Living the Poet's Life*.
*A poet toolbox full of fun facts, playful writing activities, and words of wisdom and encouragement.

Wong, Janet. 2002. *You Have to Write*.
*A poem picture book emphasizing revision and writing about everyday experiences.

Meet the Author series (published by Richard C. Owen)
Picture books in the "Meet the Author" series feature poets like Douglas Florian, Lee Bennett Hopkins, Janet Wong, and Jane Yolen talking about their lives and how they write poetry.

KINDS OF POEMS

There are several different types of poems in this book, including the following. Just for fun, try writing your own poem in one of these forms.

Acrostic Poem ("Service"; p. 87)
An acrostic poem uses the first letter of the first word of each line to create a word vertically that is often the theme or topic of the poem.

Epistolary Poem ("Stoked"; p. 59)
An epistolary poem is like a letter, often with an opening greeting and a closing signature.

Free Verse Poem ("Remembering"; p. 83)
Poets who write free verse poems do not use rhyme at the ends of lines, but they often create a rhythm with the length of lines.

List Poem ("Promise"; p. 71)
A list poem incorporates a list of items important to the poem topic.

Mask Poem ("Trust"; p. 13)
A mask poem is written from the point of view of an object, an animal, or a person that is not you (the writer).

Poem for Two Voices ("Breakfast"; p. 85)
A poem for two voices is arranged in two or more columns for reading aloud by more than one person with lines read individually or together.

Poem with Repetition ("Selfie"; p. 25)
Poets often repeat a word or phrase or line to emphaize the meaning or to maximize the sounds of the words.

Poem with Simile ("Support"; p. 41)
A poem where two or more things are compared with the words "like" or "as" (often a person compared with an animal or object).

Question Poem ("Jitters"; p. 55)
Sometimes poets ask and answer questions in a poem with whole lines posing questions to ponder.

Rhyming Poem ("Explorers"; p. 77)
Many poets use rhyme to emphasize the sounds of words – at the end of lines, in alternating lines, or even in the middle of lines.

ABOUT THE POETS

You probably found some favorite poems when reading this book. Write down the poets' names and learn more about them by visiting their websites and blogs. Then look for more of their poems (and books)!

Gail Aldous   scbwi.org/members-public/gail-aldous
Gail Aldous is a poet and former teacher who writes for children and young adults. One of her poems appears in *Things We Eat*. She loves all animals, especially puppies and kittens.

Marcie Flinchum Atkins   marcieatkins.com
Marcie Flinchum Atkins is a school librarian and the author of several nonfiction books including *Wait, Rest, Pause: Dormancy in Nature*. She loves being in or near the water – especially with friends.

Robyn Hood Black   robynhoodblack.com
Robyn Hood Black's poems appear in numerous anthologies and in leading haiku journals. She makes literary art and gifts through her business, artsyletters. She's beyond grateful for the presence of friends.

Willeena Booker   Twitter: @WilleenaB
Willeena Booker is an educator and poet. Willeena's poem "Xenial" appears in *Things We Feel* by Pomelo Books. Her poem "I Matter" is featured on Pongo Poetry Project's BIPOC Voices page. Willeena enjoys taking selfies with friends and family.

Sandy Brehl   sandybrehlbooks.com
Sandy Brehl is the author of the *Odin's Promise* WWII trilogy, picture book *Is It Over?*, and poetry in *Spider Magazine* and *Things We Eat*. She can't wait to hear about your friendships.

Carol Bullman   achildrensbookworld.com
Carol Bullman is the author of the picture book *Your Nursery Is an Everywhere*. Her family and friends are her greatest treasures!

Kelly Conroy   kellyconroy.com
Kelly Conroy is a children's book writer and poet. Her goal in life is to make people smile and she is always up for a long walk with one of her copilots.

Mary E. Cronin   maryecronin.com
Mary E. Cronin's poems have appeared in many anthologies. She is a K-2 Literacy Coach in Massachusetts who loves teaming up with readers, writers, educators, and poets.

Linda A. Dryfhout   Twitter: @LADryfhout
Linda A. Dryfhout is a poet with poems in magazines and anthologies including *Hop To It* and *Things We Eat*. Her favorite activities include sewing, and she has made many costumes for various church plays.

Janet Clare Fagal   Facebook: facebook.com/janet.clare.311
Janet Clare Fagal's poems appear in anthologies including three from Pomelo Books and one by Lee Bennett Hopkins. Camping across America during childhood taught her valuable lessons about family, friendship, and nature's beauty!

Karen Elise Finch   Twitter: @nestofbooks
Karen Elise Finch has shared her love of words and images as a preschool teacher, art educator, library assistant, and reading tutor. She remembers what it was like to be welcomed as the new kid in class and loves sharing laughs with friends.

Nancy Bo Flood   nancyboflood.com
Nancy Bo Flood grew up on a basketball court. Her dad loved the sport and, as a coach, he loved watching kids of all ages, all sizes, come together and become a team.

Patricia J. Franz   patriciajfranz.com
Patricia J. Franz is a writer and poet. Her first poem appeared in the anthology *Things We Feel*. She believes a better world must first be imagined and children will lead the way.

Marilyn Garcia   marilynrgarcia.com
Marilyn Garcia is an author and poet whose work appears in several anthologies including *Hop to It: Poems to Get You Moving*. Her favorite lacrosse stick is made of wood and leather.

Van G. Garrett   vanggarrettpoet.com
Van G. Garrett is the author of *Kicks*, a picture book about a boy selecting the perfect sneakers. Van enjoys writing and relaxing in a cabin when times turn wintry.

Theresa Gaughan   Twitter: @TheresaGaughan
Theresa Gaughan is a veteran teacher who enjoys writing and sharing poetry with her third-grade students. Hiking through the woods with friends is one of her favorite things to do.

Sara Holbrook   saraholbrook.com
Sara Holbrook lets it all out through her poetry in books and schools worldwide. Poet, author, educator, she loves writing, knitting, quilting, and connecting with students with her partner-in-rhyme, Michael Salinger.

Irene Latham   irenelatham.com
Irene Latham is a grateful creator of many books for children. She loves connecting with others via Zoom and appreciates the steady companionship of her husband Paul and their elderly cat Maggie.

Rebecca Gardyn Levington   rebeccagardynlevington.com
Rebecca Gardyn Levington is a children's book author, poet, and journalist who is grateful for all the cool technology that keeps her connected with far-flung family and friends.

Molly Lorenz   Twitter: @booksR4me
Molly Lorenz is a retired art teacher and resides in eastern Pennsylvania with her husband Bryen. She enjoys writing for children, quilting, gardening, and having lunch with friends.

Jone Rush MacCulloch   jonerushmacculloch.com/blog
Jone Rush MacCulloch is a former library media specialist and teacher who is a poet, photographer, artist, and Poetry Friday Blogger. You'll find her with her phone capturing pictures of her friends and her favorite Ollie, her grand-nephew.

Carmela A. Martino   carmelamartino.com
Carmela A. Martino is the author of two novels as well as poems and short stories published in numerous anthologies. She lives outside Chicago, IL, with her favorite sidekick, her husband John.

Guadalupe García McCall   ggmccall.com
Guadalupe García McCall is an educator and the author of many poems, short stories, and novels, including *The Keeper*. She loves nature walks and always protects her face with sunglasses and sunscreen!

Rochelle Melander   rochellemelander.com
Rochelle Melander teaches writing in schools and libraries and is the author of *Mightier Than the Sword*. She flunked the Presidential Fitness Test because she couldn't do 53 sit-ups in a minute.

Heidi Mordhorst   myjuicylittleuniverse.blogspot.com
Heidi Mordhorst is a poet and teacher specializing in early literacy programs. Her favorite way to travel is by electric bike. She spends a lot of time watching how her own brain works and tries hard to be her own best friend.

Elisabeth Norton   elisabethnorton.com
Elisabeth Norton is an English teacher and writer who loves playing with words to create poems and books for young readers. She is much better at watching tennis than playing it!

Joan Riordan   Twitter: @JRiordan173
Joan Riordan is a teacher with decades of experience. She enjoys creating, baking, and taking long walks. She is stoked to have a poem in *What Is a Friend?*

Laura Purdie Salas   laurasalas.com
Former teacher Laura Purdie Salas is a poet and author of 135+ books, including *Lion of the Sky* and *Zap! Clap! Boom!* She gets the jitters whenever a new book publishes.

René Saldaña, Jr.   renesaldanajr.blogspot.com
René Saldaña, Jr. is a professor of literacy at Texas Tech University. He has also written books for children and young adults including *The Jumping Tree* and *A Good Long Way*, and has edited the YA anthology of poetry *I Sing: The Body*, poems about body image.

Michael Salinger   michaelsalinger.com
Michael Salinger is a father, husband, sculptor, cyclist, poet, and educator. He promotes poetry in the classroom and beyond across the globe with his partner-in-rhyme Sara Holbrook.

Donna JT Smith   mainelywrite.blogspot.com
Donna lives on the coast of Maine, writing poems, painting, and collecting beach glass. Growing up, she and her siblings climbed trees and argued, but ALWAYS stood up for each other!

Anastasia Suen   asuen.com
Anastasia Suen is the author (and ghostwriter) of more than 400 books for children, teens, and adults. She believes being a friend leads to service, to helping others in need.

Pamela Taylor pamelabtaylor.com
Pamela Taylor is a former educator who is now a writer. Her poem "Determined" is in the anthology *Things We Feel*. She delights in poetry with a healthy respect for words.

Linda Kulp Trout lindakulptrout.blogspot.com
Linda Kulp Trout is a retired teacher whose poems and articles have appeared in many publications. She has always loved horses and believes they make very good friends.

Fernanda Valentino Twitter: @fgvalentino
Fernanda Valentino was raised in Perth, Australia and now lives in Chicago. Her poems have appeared in *Highlights Hello!* and *High Five Magazine*. She has also translated books from French to English. Chess is not her forté.

Charles Waters charleswaterspoetry.com
Charles Waters is the co-author (with Irene Latham) of various books of poetry including *Can I Touch Your Hair? Poems of Race, Mistakes and Friendship*. His favorite meal of the day is breakfast because it's important to get the day started off right.

Vicki Wilke winningwriters.com/people/vicki-wilke
Vicki Wilke was a K-1 teacher for 33 years while joyfully writing and publishing poetry for children and adults. Her five grandchildren fill her with happiness. She loves remembering their fun times and creating new memories.

Matthew Winter Twitter: @Baileysdad420
Matthew Winter is a first-grade teacher in New York. He loves writing poems and reading. Also, he enjoys playing (and jumping) with his best friend and poodle-son, Bailey.

Helen Kemp Zax helenzax.com
Helen Kemp Zax is a former lawyer whose poems have been published in anthologies such as *Hop to It: Poems to Get You Moving* and *Imperfect II*. Laughter has kept many friendships from her childhood alive throughout a lifetime.

Sarah Ziman sarahziman.co.uk
Sarah Ziman is an award-winning poet from the UK whose work appears regularly in magazines and anthologies. She is not great at team sports, but has some very supportive writer friends.

POEM CREDITS

Gail Aldous: "Trust"; © 2022 by Gail Aldous.
Marcie Flinchum Atkins: "Promise"; © 2022 by Marcie Flinchum Atkins.
Robyn Hood Black: "Present"; © 2022 by Robyn Hood Black.
Willeena Booker: "Selfie"; © 2022 by Willeena Booker.
Sandy Brehl: "Wait!"; © 2022 by Sandy Brehl.
Carol Bullman: "Treasured"; © 2022 by Carol Bullman.
Kelly Conroy: "Copilot"; © 2022 by Kelly Conroy.
Mary E. Cronin: "Team"; © 2022 by Mary E. Cronin.
Linda A. Dryfhout: "Action"; © 2022 by Linda A. Dryfhout.
Janet Clare Fagal: "Camping"; © 2022 by Janet Clare Fagal.
Karen Elise Finch: "New"; © 2022 by Karen Elise Finch.
Nancy Bo Flood: "Swish"; © 2022 by Nancy Bo Flood.
Patricia J. Franz: "Imagine"; © 2022 by Patricia J. Franz.
Marilyn Garcia: "Alive"; © 2022 by Marilyn Garcia.
Van G. Garrett: "Storytelling"; © 2022 by Van G. Garrett.
Theresa Gaughan: "Explorers"; © 2022 by Theresa Gaughan.
Sara Holbrook: "Instead"; © 2022 by Sara Holbrook.
Irene Latham: "Together"; © 2022 by Irene Latham.
Rebecca Gardyn Levington: "Here"; © 2022 by Rebecca Gardyn Levington.
Molly Lorenz: "Lunch"; © 2022 by Molly Lorenz.
Jone Rush MacCulloch: "Ollie"; © 2022 by Jone Rush MacCulloch.
Carmela A. Martino: "Sidekicks"; © 2022 by Carmela A. Martino.
Guadalupe García McCall: "Amiguita"; © 2022 by Guadalupe García McCall.
Rochelle Melander: "Sit-ups"; © 2022 by Rochelle Melander.
Heidi Mordhorst: "Myself"; © 2022 by Heidi Mordhorst.
Elisabeth Norton: "Winning"; © 2022 by Elisabeth Norton.
Joan Riordan: "Stoked"; © 2022 by Joan Riordan.
Laura Purdie Salas: "Jitters"; © 2022 by Laura Purdie Salas.
René Saldaña, Jr.: "Happy"; © 2022 by René Saldaña, Jr.
Michael Salinger: "Freewheeling"; © 2022 by Michael Salinger.
Donna JT Smith: "Siblings"; © 2022 by Donna JT Smith.
Anastasia Suen: "Service"; © 2022 by Anastasia Suen.
Pamela Taylor: "Gamers"; © 2022 by Pamela Taylor.
Linda Kulp Trout: "Rescue"; © 2022 by Linda Kulp Trout.
Fernanda Valentino: "Checkmate"; © 2022 by Fernanda Valentino.

ABOUT VARDELL & WONG

Sylvia M. Vardell recently retired as Professor in the School of Library and Information Studies at Texas Woman's University where she taught graduate courses in children's and young adult literature for more than 20 years. Vardell has published extensively, including five books on literature for children as well as over 25 book chapters and 100 journal articles. She is so grateful for all the poets she gets to work with – especially her friend Janet Wong. Learn more about Vardell at SylviaVardell.com.

Janet Wong is a graduate of Yale Law School and a former lawyer. She has written more than 35 books for children on a wide variety of subjects, including chess (*Alex and the Wednesday Chess Club*) and yoga (*Twist: Yoga Poems*). She is the 2021 winner of the NCTE Excellence in Poetry for Children Award, a lifetime achievement award that is one of the highest honors a children's poet can receive. Janet considers Sylvia to be one of her best friends; even though they disagree on many things, she can always trust Sylvia to be kind, fair, and fun. Learn more about Janet at JanetWong.com.

Together, Vardell & Wong are the creative forces behind Pomelo Books.

ABOUT POMELO BOOKS

Pomelo Books is Poetry PLUS. Poetry PLUS play. Poetry PLUS science. Poetry PLUS holidays. Poetry PLUS pets – and more. We make it EASY to share poetry any time of day.

Successful K-12 teachers and administrators build regular "touch points" into their routines to create a safe and engaging learning environment. Poetry can be a powerful tool for offering a shared literary experience in just a few minutes, with both curricular benefits and emotional connections for students at all levels.

Our books in The Poetry Friday Anthology series and the Poetry Friday Power Book series make it easy to use poetry for integrating skills, building language learning, crossing curricular areas, mentoring young writers, promoting critical thinking, fostering social-emotional development, and inviting students to respond creatively. A shared poetry moment can help build a classroom community filled with kindness, respect, and joy. Learn more at PomeloBooks.com.

The Poetry of Science
An NSTA Recommends selection
"A treasury of the greatest science poetry for children ever written, with a twist." NSTA

The Poetry of Science is an illustrated book for children that contains 250 poems on science, technology, engineering, and math organized by topic.

Great Morning! Poems for School Leaders to Read Aloud
A CBC Hot Off the Press selection

75 poems for morning announcements or for the start of class or just to take a "brain break" when you need it! Principals, teachers, and student leaders will find poems on many useful topics from school safety to celebrating the teamwork of teachers and staff members such as the school nurse or custodian.

Things We Eat
A CBC Hot Off the Press selection

What things do we love to eat? In this book you'll find poems from A to Z, featuring food names and photos that will make kids want to eat an AVOCADO, BAGEL, COOKIE, ZUCCHINI, and more as you read these delicious poems.

MORE FROM POMELO BOOKS

HERE WE GO: A Poetry Friday Power Book
An NCTE Poetry Notable
An NNSTOY Social Justice Book

How can kids change the world? By practicing kindness, raising a garden that unites a community, thinking about the news, and more. This story in poems (with activities to get us drawing, talking, and writing) will guide kids as they discover their power to make an impact.

HOP TO IT: Poems to Get You Moving
A Kids' Book Choice Award "Best Book of Facts" Winner

This anthology of 100 poems by 90 poets gets kids thinking and moving as they use pantomime, sign language, and whole body movements, including deskercise! You'll also find poems on current topics, such as life during a pandemic. Take a 30-second indoor recess whenever you need it!

The Poetry Friday Anthology for Celebrations
ILA Notable Books for a Global Society

This fun book features 156 poems (in both Spanish & English) honoring a wide variety of traditional and non-traditional holidays from all over the world. Also available in a Teacher/Librarian Edition.

"A bubbly and educational bilingual poetry anthology for children." – Kirkus

YOU JUST WAIT: A Poetry Friday Power Book
A CBC Hot Off the Press selection
An NCTE Poetry Notable

Twelve poems by poets such as Joseph Bruchac and Margarita Engle are joined into a story with poems about identity, sports, food, and movies.

"Young readers will find their fingers itching to respond to these verses." – Carol Jago, Past President of NCTE

Made in the USA
Monee, IL
05 October 2022

15287109R00061